A 'Head of Steam'

A humorous look at today's heritage railways

Written & Illustrated by Alan Ward

To Jackie best wishes Alan x

Alandi Publications

A 'Head of Steam'
A Humorous Look at Today's Heritage Railways
Written & Illustrated by Alan Ward

ISBN 978-0-9555187-0-6

Designed, produced & published by
ALANDI PUBLICATIONS
2 Woodpecker Crescent, Pucklechurch BS16 9ST

Printed in England
Superior, Melksham, Wiltshire

For every book sold, a donation of 50p will be made to
The Macmillan Cancer Support Fund

FOREWORD

I am delighted to write these few lines as the introduction to this book of Alan Ward's cartoons. It is always difficult to come up with a different angle to depict the subject of 'heritage railways' because, in this digital age, just about anything and everything which is done under the guise of railway heritage is now portrayed (often several times over!) in railway periodicals, books, videos, dvds, or on the web! So it is good that Alan has hit on the idea of portraying the subject by way of this series of cartoons.

When it comes to the subject of 'railways', I confess to being one of those who look to our heritage railways as representing a reassuring 'thread of continuity' in this ever changing world. As a frequent user of today's transport system, I now look back with far more favour to the railway system that existed in my earlier years.

This book of Alan's cartoons will provide much light relief, not only amongst those who contribute to the ever growing popularity and importance of our heritage railways, but to a much wider audience. Perhaps today's rail commuters should each be commended to purchase a copy as some much needed light relief when next travelling to and from work by train (that's always assuming there will be space available to turn the pages)!

It is entirely appropriate that Alan has chosen to launch this book at the 2007 Spring Gala on the West Somerset Railway; a 'premier' organisation (and, I admit, a personal favourite) which, deservedly, has been given - for the third year running - a top national heritage 'Railway of the Year' award.

Mike Arlett

INTRODUCTION

During over twenty years as a professional wildlife and railway artist
I have been involved in many aspects of the Heritage Railway movement.
The dedication of the volunteers and staff never ceases to amaze me.
People give of their time, mostly without reward, save for the satisfaction of seeing
so many ambitious projects come to fruition. We have encountered interesting and absorbing
characters and are fortunate to count many of them as friends.

I would like to thank Diana Schuch, my partner; soul mate; editor; sounding board
and best friend. Without her, I doubt that this book would have been published

Having completed our first cartoon book on home shopping and network marketing,
our thoughts turned to a second, and what better subject than 'heritage railways'.
Many of the humorous situations encountered in this respect came to mind.

A 'Head of Steam' rapidly built-up and cartoons began to flow.
It was mind-broadening and, often, side-splitting when people
began to relate their own personal experiences. We thank them for finding time to
share them with us. Many have found their way into the book.
Some, we have to say, are a little risque'. A lot are tongue in cheek, but we hope
you will enjoy them nonetheless. If you recognise a bit of yourself in the book,
we make no apologies whatsoever.
Have fun reading.

Alan Ward

1

"I feel a little bit uneasy about going on this Murder Mystery Special"

What did the big engine say to the little engine?
You're too young to smoke!

"Hey Fred,
pass me
the shower gel!"

4

"Arthur, will you please keep still whilst I take this shot before the farmer sees us!"

"What is it today George, Mocha, Latte or Costa Rican Dark Roast?"

"Now I know why they put these old platform
trolleys back on the station !"

"Who's idea was it to invite kids onto the footplate?"

10

11

"What's all that noise?"

*"Haven't you heard, it's
'Thomas the Talk Engine' Day!"*

"Yes sir,
the 10.25 is
definitely
Steam Hauled"

"I hope you don't mind me asking, but are you anticipating some mainline running problems?"

"He's complaining that the sandwich is <u>too fresh.</u> He ordered a traditional-style BR one with the crusts turned up!"

FRIENDLY RIVALRY

"*Do you think Santa's worked on a heritage railway before?*"

23

"Just remember son, in forty-odd years time, you will sit proudly on the gleaming footplate with all the other children"

"WOW........
what a
Woman!!!"

27

*"Water's a bit
cold this morning
Charles!"*

28

"Oh, he's alright.
Says he takes better pictures when he
re-lives the past!"

29

"You'll never believe it Sarge, we've just been overtaken by the Flying Scotsman!"

TOILET

ENGAGED

COUGH COUGH

WHO WANTS TO BE A MILLIONAIRE RAILWAY VERSION

QUESTIONS

*	50/50
*	Phone a friend
*	Ask the audience

£100 Question:
When is the best time to travel?

| A | Rush Hour | B | Never |
| C | When strike is on | D | At Night |

£500,000 Question:
Who broke-up the railways?

| A | Railtrack | B | Irish Labour |
| C | Virgin | D | Dr. Beeching |

£1,000.000 Question:
Who invented 'Rocket'?

| A | Guy Fawkes | B | Stephenson |
| C | NASA | D | Percy Thrower |

*Surprise, surprise, there are no prizes for getting it right. It's for fun. Shame on you.

33

*HOW DO YOU SPOT
A TRAINSPOTTER?*

THE RAT RACE SPECIAL

<u>Jokes</u>

"I say, I say Porter, where is Fish-hook?"
"It's at the end of the line sir!"

What did the Sleeper say to the Cradle? *Wake me up before your next feed!*

What's a twack? *It's a thing that twains run on!*

What did the platform say to the track?
You run on ahead while I hold these people up!

What ticks on the station office wall? *Ticky paper!*   (*boom, boom.........!*)

"I don't think it was such a good idea getting engineers from all the regions to work on this restoration project!"

"I didn't quite expect this when we booked the Fish & Chip Supper Special!"

"One adult and two children returns please"

"Something to take home as a reminder
of your visit to the railway?
I've got just the thing for you sir!"

"Ahhhh..........
yes, '55,
a classic vintage!"

"You said it was a
Forces Re-enactment Weekend"
*"I'm sorry, I got the dates mixed up
with Thomas the Tank Engine Day!"*

"I say my man, it's a great pity they didn't
build the station closer to the village"
*"Yes madam, but they decided it was better to build it close to the
railway line!"*

"Hang-on driver,
just another twenty minutes
or so, and I'll
be finished!"

"The exchange rate's gone up Bert. It's now four lumps of coal to one basket of mushrooms!"

46

"Hello dear.
There, I wasn't that long was I?
I've got some marvellous pictures......"

"I really don't know what they see
in this 'eritage railway lark!"

"Fish and Chip Specials, Murder Mystery Specials, Carol Train Specials.......it had to happen didn't it?"

"*I don't care what you say, this Polish coal doesn't steam properly!*"

55

*Remind me darling,
which railway are we on,
heritage or network?"*

"Who do you think
the fine will go to, the heritage railway
or the local council?"

"*Driver,
do you think
it might be a bit easier
to use the mobile to call
for assistance?*"

"WHAT **!!!@@*** LUNATIC CLEANED OUT THE WATER TANKS WITH DETERGENT?"

COUNTY CLASS KING CLASS WORKING CLASS

"The train now arriving on platform 1.
is very tired, short of coal and water, has a
grumpy driver; is one hour, forty minutes late
and the lady guard's husband has got
fed up waiting for her.
What do we say?......."

AAAHH!!!!

"What's the problem?"
"Oh...........
it's alright, just a
hot axlebox."

63

"How long did they
say they would be?"
*"They couldn't be sure because
they're very busy, but possibly
within the hour."*
"OK, It's your lead!"

MILK TRAIN   GRAVY TRAIN   MAIL TRAIN

"Old George loves these office Christmas party bookings"

FOR THAT VERY SPECIAL OCCASION, WHY NOT HOLD YOUR WEDDING RECEPTION AT YOUR LOCAL HERITAGE RAILWAY?

"Relax, it's an old beauty spot, and besides, this line's been disused since 1968!"

"Dad, is there something you're not telling me about Thomas?"

"Good evening sir. We've had a slight problem. I wonder if you might place a few of these around the yard?"

"Tom, do you want a touch more coal dust and grease garnish on your sausage sarnie?"

74

"Mum, are you sure that's a proper Santa hat?"

75

"What the hell is that guard doing?"
"Oh, don't worry, he's just retired from the navy. It's semaphore. He's telling us he'll get the tea in at the next station!"

"Grand order of Rats, I have called this EGM because we have been served with an eviction order from the Procrastination Preservation Society. They are finally going to start work ————— on the first of next month!"

"Phew..............
that was a long, dark,
dirty and dank tunnel
wasn't it Jim?"

79

"Ernie, this geezer 'ere would like to know what we'd do with a Caprotti valve gear motion?"

"Don't you think these 'best-kept station garden' competitions are getting a bit out of hand?"

"I said paint it British Rail Black, then lined out...... not BRITISH RAIL BLACK LINES THROUGHOUT!"

"Do you think they'll notice that we're short of coach sets for the gala?"

"More steam Bill, it's Station Master's uniform inspection today!"

THE FLYING SCOTSMAN

THE CATHEDRALS EXPRESS

"*Phew, thank goodness, that's the last train. No more sparks until the spring!*"

88

"Darling...
I don't think they
had a piece of coal in
mind when they asked
for donations!"

"Darling, is it normal to take down numbers in a notebook at these heritage railway events?"

"Yes, of course it is darling."

"Well, don't look now, but, there's someone behind you writing down the number on your rugby shirt!"

"*Don't you think we ought to turn the vacuum brake system off?*"

"This was not what I thought you had in mind when you told me you'd booked the 'Rail'n Cruise' special!"

"................................Where was I?,
Oh yes! It was 1956, or was it 1957? That's
right, it was 1957. Well, this train came
through Throgmorton Central with the
most unusual set of coaches
I've ever seen. I remember
the serial numbers of
every single coach to this
day. They were:
000127354/0045
& 23304567+
21346694700
00345330+ ...
00231456684
3300069.........
................."

Alan has spent most of his life in the
West Country, particularly in the
Bristol, Weston-super-Mare and
Exmoor areas. He has painted all his
life and has been a full time
 professional artist since 1985.
He is well-known for his Railway,

Marine and Wildlife paintings, many of them commissions. A large
number of these are published as fine art and limited edition prints.
Several exhibitions are held throughout the year in various locations.
For more information, or to contact Alan, please visit
www.alanwardcollection.co.uk
email: info@alanwardcollection.co.uk